11+ CSSE Essex

Practice Papers

2 Full Sets of Mock Practice
Papers For the Eleven Plus
CSSE Essex Test

11+ CSSE Examination For Grammar School Admissions

CSSE Test

11+ CSSE Examination Practice Papers

Instructions, Guidance, Practice Papers & Answers

CONTENTS

As part of this product you have also received FREE access to online tests that will help you to pass the 11+.

To gain access, simply go to:

www.MyEducationalTests.co.uk

Get more products for passing any test at:

www.How2Become.com

Orders: Please contact How2Become Ltd, Suite 1, 60 Churchill Square Business Centre, Kings Hill, Kent ME19 4YU.

You can order through Amazon.co.uk under ISBN: 9781912370269, via the website www.How2Become.com or through Gardners.com.

ISBN: 9781912370269

First published in 2018 by How2Become Ltd.

Copyright © 2018 How2Become.

Typeset by Katie Noakes for How2Become Ltd.

Disclaimer

Every effort has been made to ensure that the information contained within this guide is accurate at the time of publication. How2Become Ltd is not responsible for anyone failing any part of any selection process as a result of the information contained within this guide. How2Become Ltd and their authors cannot accept any responsibility for any errors or omissions within this guide, however caused. No responsibility for loss or damage occasioned by any person acting, or refraining from action, as a result of the material in this publication can be accepted by How2Become Ltd.

The information within this guide does not represent the views of any third party service or organisation.

The CSSE Test

Hello, and welcome to your CSSE 11+ Examination Practice Papers Guide. Written by the UK's leading career specialists, this book provides a comprehensive insight into the CSSE 11+ Examination, including sample practice papers to help you on your way to passing your 11+. It will ensure that students are fully prepared for their test, and allow them to practice using sample questions.

Here at How2Become, we strive to ensure that students and parents are satisfied with our guides, and to produce outstanding books that are packed full of advice and tips. This book will give you everything you need to know, and more, about the CSSE 11+ Examination.

WHAT IS THE CSSE II+ EXAMINATION?

As of September 2014, the Government introduced a new and challenging 11+, which students must pass if they wish to attend grammar school. The CSSE 11+ Examination is an adopted version of the previous 11+, which assesses abilities in numerical and literary understanding. The CSSE 11+ Examination has been modified to ensure that all students, no matter what their background, have a fair and equal chance of passing the test. The CSSE 11+ Examination is designed to assess whether grammar school is a suitable choice for pupils who wish to attend.

The CSSE 11+ Examination has two main sections:

- MATHS TEST
- ENGLISH TEST
    - o   Section 1 – Comprehension
    - o   Section 2 – Applied Reasoning
    - o   Section 3 – Continuous Writing

WHO TAKES THE CSSE ESSEX 11+?

The consortium of selective schools in Essex requires you to take two tests (one English, one Maths) in order to gain entry into any of the following ten schools:

1. **Colchester County High School for Girls.**

2. **Colchester Royal Grammar School.**

3. **King Edward VI Grammar School.**

4. **Shoeburyness High School.**

5. **Southend High School for Boys.**

6. **Southend High School for Girls.**

7. **St. Bernard's High School for Girls.**

8. **St. Thomas More High School for Boys.**

9. **Westcliff High School for Boys.**

10. **Westcliff High School for Girls.**

HOW IS THE CSSE ESSEX SCORED?

To be given a grammar school placement, students need to score a total of 320 out of a possible 420. No single score can be below the score mark of 106.

The score for the CSSE Test will vary every year. Therefore there is no set score that needs to be met in order to gain a place in a grammar school. The score is set each year depending on the performance of all of the students taking the test. In other words, if the majority of students scored highly, the pass mark would be higher. If the majority of students scored low, the pass mark would be lower.

WHERE SHOULD THE ANSWERS BE WRITTEN?

For the real test, students will be provided with two booklets. One booklet will be the testing booklet which will include all the questions. The other booklet is the answer booklet and should be filled out in relation to the testing questions. Students need to check that you have been given the correct testing and answer booklets and it is the paper that you are expected to sit.

In the actual test, to mark the correct answer in the answer booklet, students must draw a line through the small rectangular box, indicating their chosen answer.

Like so:

Remember, students' answers must show correlation with the number of the correct question. You will not receive a mark for the question, if your answer number doesn't match the question number.

STRUCTURE OF THE BOOK

This book follows a simple structure, in order to help parents guide their children through each stage of the CSSE Test assessment process.

The structure of our CSSE 11+ Examination Practice Papers Guide is as follows:

- Maths
    o Section 1 – Maths – comprised of basic arithmetic-style questions.
    o Section 2 – Maths – comprised of more challenging mathematical questions including graphs and charts.
- English
    o Section 1 - Comprehension – comprised of reading a text and answering questions.
    o Section 2 – Applied Reasoning – comprised of literary reasoning skills.
    o Section 3 – Continuous Writing – comprised of a creative writing task.

Finally, we have also provided you with some additional free online psychometric tests which will help to further improve your competence in this particular testing area. To gain access, simply go to:

www.MyEducationalTests.co.uk

ABOUT THE CSSE TEST

Below we have outlined what you can expect from each 11+ paper:

English Test

The English test will be divided into three main sections:

1. Comprehension.

2. Applied reasoning.

3. Continuous writing.

You are given a total of one hour and ten minutes to complete the exam.

Here is a quick breakdown of what each of these sections consist of, and how the exam board recommends you utilise your time.

1. Comprehension

This section requires you to read a passage or an extract of text, and subsequently answer a range of questions based upon what you have just read.

For the real exam it is recommended that you spend approximately ten minutes reading the extract given, and a further thirty minutes answering the related questions.

The lines of the text will be numbered in order for you to be able to refer back to them when giving your answers.

The types of questions that you will be asked in the comprehension section are designed to test your understanding of the text and the words and themes within it. They will be a combination of both multiple choice and longer, more descriptive questions.

2. Applied Reasoning

It is recommended that you spend ten minutes on this part of the test in the real exam. During this section, you will be asked a few different types of 'verbal reasoning' style questions.

Given the time frame in which you have to answer these questions, you will have to complete them fairly quickly. They will involve more 'quick fire' type exercises and they will be prefaced with an example question and answer, so that you can get an idea of what the question is asking of you.

3. Continuous Writing

You will be given a separate booklet for this part of the test. It is recommended that you spend around twenty minutes completing this section in the real exam.

You will be set a couple of tasks, and then asked to write a number of sentences (around six or seven) on a subject or topic in your own words.

It makes sense to divide your time evenly for these two questions, so with that in mind you should aim to spend around ten minutes answering each one.

For these questions, you will be assessed on the creativity and quality of the pieces you write, along with the correct and proper usage of punctuation and spelling.

WHAT WILL BE TESTED?

The English part of this test will focus on everything pupils have been taught during their English classes. The English paper will extensively look at grammar, punctuation, spelling and comprehension in order to evaluate their literary abilities and skills. The test will focus on literary elements such as:

- Correcting the following sentences;
- Grammar, spelling and punctuation;
- Reading and comprehension;
- Missing words;
- The right words;
- Adjectives, nouns, and verbs.

The Maths test is comprised of one test and one answer booklet is provided.

There are a total of sixty marks available for the exam, and you are given sixty minutes to complete the test.

It is recommended that you answer all the questions you can. Don't spend too long on a question that you are not sure on. If there's time at the end of the exam, go back and try to answer any questions that you were unsure of the first time around.

You will not be able to use a calculator during the test and you will be provided with space on the answer booklet to show your workings if necessary.

The test will include an array of different types of Maths problems you will have studied at school.

The exam board advise that once the test has commenced, you will be unable to ask about any of the questions within it.

The number of available marks for each question will be given in the margin of each page.

The Mathematical part of this test will draw upon mathematical equations, procedures and terminology to demonstrate numerical understanding and ability. However, the mathematical style of such questions remain similar. They focus on particular areas such as:

- Fractions;
- Multiplication;
- Division;
- Charts and graphs;
- Number sequences;
- Areas and perimeters;
- Shapes and angles.

Guidance for the 11+

CSSE II+ EXAMINATION - GENERAL TIPS FOR STUDENTS

- The exam is designed specifically to test the kind of things you will have been learning in your Maths lessons at Key Stage 2. Therefore, it is important to brush up on all the key skills you have been working on at school, as well as trying your hand at some example practice questions such as those covered in this book.

- Ensure you understand what each question is asking you before you start to answer it. Re-read a question if you are unsure.

- Make sure you allocate your time in the exam wisely. Whilst it is important to make sure you understand and spend enough time on each question to get the best marks, you don't want to end up rushing any questions at the end of the paper.

- When you are given your test paper it will have recommended amounts of time to spend on each section of the exam. Whilst these times are only given as a guide, bear in mind that they have been formulated to try and help you make the most of your time, so try to stick to them wherever possible.

- The amount of marks that can be awarded for each question will be given in the margins of the test paper. This should also be an indicator for how long you should be spending on each question. Generally speaking, the higher the amount of marks you are able to get, the longer you should be spending answering the question.

- If you get really stuck on a question, don't spend too long thinking about it. Instead, move on to answering the rest of the paper to the best of your abilities, and leave some time at the end to come back and re-visit any questions you were unsure about the first time around.

- Make sure you practise all of the different types of questions before the exam. If there are certain types of questions you find harder to answer, or topics you struggle with, spend a little more time practising them than the ones you find easier.

TIPS FOR PARENTS

✓ You may believe that the onus is really on your child's school to prepare them for their upcoming exam. While this is the case to some extent, it has been shown that parents' support and encouragement for their child to do even a small amount of practice outside of school can really improve their performance.

✓ Do not overload your child with stacks of work and make them feel overwhelmed. This will only serve to discourage them. As with many things, it is best to aim to break up their revision sessions into small, manageable chunks. This will ensure that their concentration levels remain high and they are able to take in the information that is being covered.

✓ Following on from the last point, make sure you schedule in plenty of rest breaks for your child. Allow them to go outside or participate in an activity that they enjoy doing. This boosts their energy and prepares them for the next time they sit down to study.

✓ Reward their progress and achievements. This doesn't have to mean anything extravagant, but when they have done well, or mastered a certain type of question that they had been struggling with, a small reward will make it all feel worthwhile.

✓ Have key notes or definitions placed around your home or your child's bedroom so that they are there to glance at every now and then. This will refresh the memory subliminally and help small portions of information to sink in. Visual aids are a great way to stimulate a child's brain.

✓ Encourage your child not to feel embarrassed about speaking up regarding topics they don't understand, so that they are able to talk through them.

✓ Plan to focus on a specific topic in each 'session'. This will ensure that it is not too overwhelming and your child's focus is set. Begin with a topic that they find the most challenging and interchange this with a topic that they are confident on – this will keep their confidence at a stable level.

✓ Encourage note-taking and bullet-point making. If your child is simply reading through questions and working them out in their head, or speaking aloud the answers, it is less likely that the information will be retained than if it is written down.

- ✓ Make sure your child has an environment to study in which is as distraction free as possible. Somewhere not too noisy or cluttered will be the most productive kind of environment for them to work in. This will also mean that they will get more done as they avoid potential interruptions.

- ✓ Similarly, when your child has set aside some time to revise, make sure that the television is off, there are no phones available, and the focus is purely on the subject for that period of time. This means that once it is time for a break, these things will serve as a kind of reward for them in their free time.

- ✓ Once your child has become confident with a certain type of question, try encouraging them to practise under timed conditions. They do not necessarily have to do a whole past paper in one sitting, but even just a section whilst being timed will help to give them an idea of what it will feel like on the day of the exam.

- ✓ Gradually build up to longer sessions. If your child is having trouble concentrating, start with short twenty minute sessions and aim to build them up over the course of their exam preparation in small steps. This makes a lot more sense than sitting your child down for an hour or two and expecting them to stay concentrated from the outset.

- ✓ It may sound obvious, but make sure your child is getting enough sleep. If you haven't already, try and establish a solid routine. This will mean that they are able to concentrate and retain more information.

- ✓ It is especially important to try and ensure that your child gets adequate sleep the night before the exam. Try not to make them feel too stressed or pressured in the evening, and reassure them that you are confident in their abilities. This will alleviate some of the worrying that can occur in the days leading up to the exam.

- ✓ Let your child know that you are proud of them - whatever the outcome. They do not need the added pressure of worrying about potential failure. The best thing you can do is to encourage them.

- ✓ Getting the right nutrition is also essential for everything from concentration, to sleep, to mood. Ensure your child is eating healthily and has a well-balanced diet. Consuming too much sugar or high-fat foods will make your child's energy levels peak and then crash and thus negatively affecting their performance.

- ✓ Similarly, make sure your child is getting plenty of fresh air and exercise. They should be spending a small amount of time outside each day. This will also keep their concentration levels high and help them to get a refreshing sleep every night.

- ✓ Try not to leave revision to the last minute. This will only make your child feel unnecessarily stressed and anxious. If you start introducing small, manageable bites of revision a good amount of time before the exam, it will make for a much more productive outcome in the long run.

- ✓ In summary, we recommend positively encouraging your child, helping them to revise gradually and progressively over time. Also, it's extremely important that you constantly aim to increase their confidence. Make sure they are getting everything they need at home such as a comfortable environment to study in and a well-balanced diet, and reward them for their achievements. We wish you and your child the best of luck in their exams!

Using Your Papers

Read the **instructions** carefully before working through your CSSE 11+ Examination Practice Papers.

In this book, there are two SETS of practice papers:

Set A and Set B

Each set includes:

Paper 1 - Maths   Marks out of 60
1 hour

Paper 2 - English   Marks out of 60
1 hour and 10 minutes

Please note that the above marks are just a generic marking system, and do NOT reflect that actual mark scheme of your real exam.

Following on from the practice papers, we have also provided a whole section on 'Answering the Questions'. This will help parents and children familiarise themselves with how questions will be answered.

This book follows a simple structure, in order to help parents guide their children through each stage of the Essex 11+ Practice Papers assessment process.

- English and Maths

    o Paper 1 – Maths – comprised of arithmetic and data interpretation testing questions.

    o Paper 2 – English – comprised of three sub-sections of testing questions and answers.

Finally, we have also provided you with some additional free online educational tests which will help to further improve your competence in this particular testing area. To gain access, simply go to:

www.MyEducationalTests.co.uk

11+ CSSE TEST
Maths

SET A

Practice Paper 1 - Maths

60 minutes

First Name	
Middle Name	
Last Name	
School	
Date of Birth	

READ THE INSTRUCTIONS CAREFULLY

- Do not open your booklet until you are told to do so.
- Work as quickly as you can through ALL the questions.
- You have 60 minutes to answer ALL the questions.
- Calculators are NOT permitted during the test.

QUESTION 1

a) Calculate: 987 + 2,145

	ANSWER
987 2145 3132 4 r	3152 ✗

1 mark

b) Add 15.09 and 6.85

	ANSWER
1 5.09 6. 85 21. 94	21.94 ✓

1 mark

QUESTION 2

a) Work out the difference between: 7,985 and 657

	ANSWER
7 9⁷8̸5̸ ·657 7328	7,328 ✓

1 mark

b) Calculate: 46 × 150

	ANSWER
1 50 900 46 6000 900 6900 6800 2	6,900 ✓

1 mark

QUESTION 3

a) What is the result of 13 multiplied by 5.04?

	ANSWER
$\begin{array}{r} 5.04 \\ 13 \\ \hline 1512 \\ 50.40 \\ \hline 65.52 \end{array}$	6.552

1 mark

b) Calculate: 306 ÷ 18

	ANSWER
$18\overline{)306}$ 180 10 90 5 270 12	17

1 mark

QUESTION 4

a) Divide 552 by 24

	ANSWER
$24\overline{)552}$ 023	23

1 mark

$16 \div .8 =$
$21 \div 3 = 70$

b) Calculate: 21 ÷ 0.3

	ANSWER
$21\overline{)0.3}$	70

1 mark

Each of the following calculations is incomplete. Each calculation contains a question mark (?). Work out the value of the question mark.

QUESTION 5

a) 64 + 843 = 90?

	ANSWER
843 64 907	7 ✓

1 mark

b) 0.16 + 1.?8 = 1.74

	ANSWER
1.ᵧ4 0.16 − 1.58	5 ✓

1 mark

c) 8,?74 − 321 = 8,653

	ANSWER
8 653 321 + 8 974	9

1 mark

d) $? - 12 = -8$

	ANSWER
	4

e) $17 × 26? = 4,505$

	ANSWER
	5

f) $5.5 ÷ 2 = ?.75$

	ANSWER
	1

QUESTION 6

Finley draws a graph which shows the flight of his remote-control aeroplane.

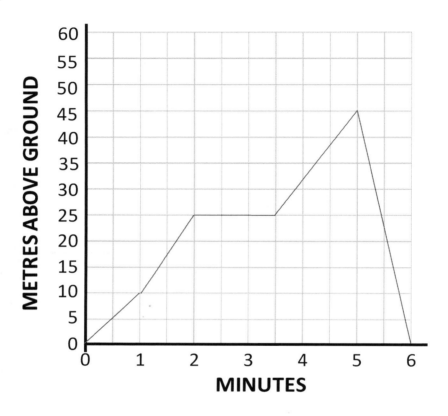

a) How long did the whole flight last for?

	ANSWER
	6 min

1 mark

b) How high was Finley's aeroplane after 5 minutes?

	ANSWER
	45 Metres above

1 mark

c) How long did it take for the aeroplane to reach 10 metres?

	ANSWER
	1 minute

1 mark

QUESTION 7

These questions show the nets of three unfolded dice. Using each net, work out how many dots would appear on the face OPPOSITE the side with 3 dots.

a)

1 mark

b)

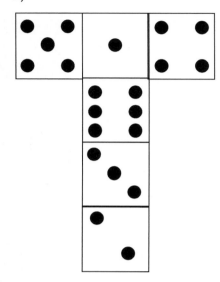

c)

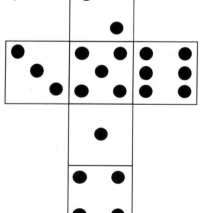

QUESTION 8

In these next questions, the letters of the alphabet have the same number values (A = 1, B = 2, C = 3, D = 4 and so on). You must multiply the numbers to reach your answers.

For example, the word FEED = 6 × 5 × 5 × 4 = a value of 600.

a) What is the total of the word PRAY?

	ANSWER

1 mark

b) List the below words in order of their total, beginning with the lowest.

| MEET | LAMB | MATE | LIAR |

1._____ 2._____ 3._____ 4._____

1 mark

c) Which single letter has the same value as the result of dividing the sum total for 'NEW' by the sum total of 'BAD'? This question requires you to add the letters together as opposed to multiplying them.

NEW ÷ BAD =

	ANSWER

1 mark

QUESTION 9

Below is a recipe which shows how to make a delicious fruit smoothie for 6 people.

- 900 ml apple juice
- 3 mangoes
- 3 bananas
- 6 oranges
- 300 ml of milk

a) How many bananas would you need to make a fruit smoothie for just 2 people?

	ANSWER
	1

1 mark

b) How many mangoes and oranges would you need to make a fruit smoothie for 60 people?

	ANSWER
	90

1 mark

QUESTION 10

Study the line graph below and work out if the statement is true or false. Tick the box that applies.

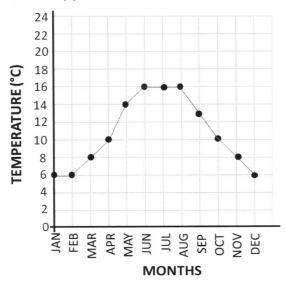

a) The lowest temperature is 4°C.

TRUE	FALSE

b) The difference between the highest and the lowest temperature is 10°C.

TRUE	FALSE

c) The temperature rose 6°C from April to June.

TRUE	FALSE

d) The largest fall in temperature was from November to December.

TRUE	FALSE

QUESTION 11

Which of the following images shows three quarters shaded in? Tick ONE answer.

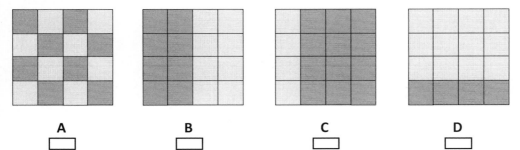

A	B	C	D
☐	☐	☐	☐

1 mark

QUESTION 12

Using the digits below, complete the challenge.

49379

a) What is the largest odd 5-digit number that you can make?

	ANSWER

1 mark

b) What is the smallest odd 5-digit number that you can make?

	ANSWER

1 mark

c) What is the smallest even 5-digit number that you can make?

	ANSWER

QUESTION 13

Below is a right-angled triangular tile:

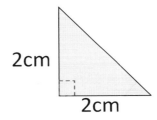

2cm

2cm

Work out how many tiles you can fit into each shape:

a)

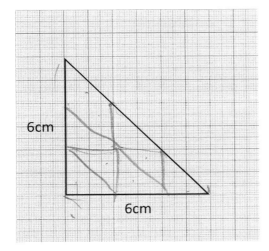

6cm

6cm

b)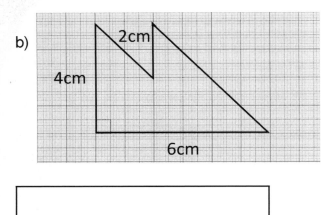

1 mark

QUESTION 14

Leah is fascinated with ladybirds. She counted how many ladybirds she could find each day for a week. Her results are shown in the pictogram below.

Monday	🐞 🐞 🐞 🐞
Tuesday	🐞 🐞 🐞 🐞
Wednesday	🐞 🐞 🐞 🐞 🐞 🐞
Thursday	🐞 🐞 🐞
Friday	🐞 🐞 🐞

Key: 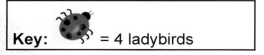 = 4 ladybirds

32

a) How many ladybirds did Leah see altogther?

	ANSWER

b) What is the average number of ladybirds Leah saw per day?

	ANSWER

QUESTION 15

Femi is hosting a competition to raise money for charity. He sells raffle tickets at his school with values from 1 to 40. The winning ticket will receive a prize.

a) Millie buys 2 tickets. What is the probability of her winning the prize?

	ANSWER

b) Millie's friend Poppy says to her that she is twice as likely to have a ticket with a prime number as one with a factor of 12. Is Poppy correct?

	ANSWER

c) Poppy also says to Millie that she is more likely to have a ticket with a prime number than one which is a multiple of 3. Is Poppy still correct?

	ANSWER

QUESTION 16

In the grid below, each number in the middle of a row or column is the mean of the numbers either side of it.

Work out the value of the shaded box.

1.4		2.2
0.2		1.2

QUESTION 17

Eight children took a test. Their scores were as follows:

56   50   52   61   67   60   60   32

a)   What was the mean score?

	ANSWER

1 mark

b)   What is the range?

	ANSWER

1 mark

QUESTION 18

For the following questions, there is one digit wrong in each calculation. They can be corrected by changing one digit in each question to the number **4**.

For the following questions, find out which digit should be replaced and re-write the calculation underneath so that it is correct.

a) 50 − 32 = 16

b) 211 + 389 = 800

c) 30 + (12 × 3) = 70

d) 3,976 + (10 × 50) = 4,376

QUESTION 19

Finish shading in the diagram below. Colour only four more squares so that the image shows one line of symmetry.

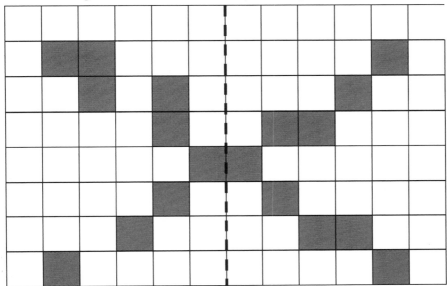

1 mark

QUESTION 20

Four-sided shapes are known as quadrilaterals. Thinking about these different four-sided shapes, decide whether the following statements are true or false.

a) All quadrilaterals are parrallelograms.

TRUE	FALSE

1 mark

b) All parallelograms are quadrilaterals.

TRUE	FALSE

1 mark

c) A parallelogram with 4 perpendicular diagonals is called a rhombus.

TRUE	FALSE

QUESTION 21

Use all four playing cards to create a correct calculation.

| 2 | 2 | 8 | 4 |

$\boxed{} \times \boxed{1}\ \boxed{} = \boxed{}\ \boxed{}$

QUESTION 22

a) Which whole number is both an even number and a prime number?

b) Write down all of the even numbers up to 50 that are also square numbers.

	ANSWER

c) Which three prime numbers multiply together to make the sum 165.

	ANSWER

1 mark

QUESTION 23

This question uses the number sequence of add 1, subtract 3, add 2, subtract 3, add 3, subtract 3,...

The first six terms in the sequence are:

$$5 \quad 6 \quad 3 \quad 5 \quad 2 \quad 5$$

a) Work out the seventh term in the sequence.

	ANSWER

1 mark

b) Work out the fifteenth term in the sequence.

	ANSWER

1 mark

c) Work out the twentieth term in the sequence.

	ANSWER

QUESTION 24

a) Abbie is shopping for clothes in the sale. She finds a dress she likes. The original price was £65.00. There is a tag on the dress saying it is now 25% off. How much is the dress?

	ANSWER

b) Abbie's friend tells her that tomorrow the shop will put a 30% discount on the dress. How much money would Abbie save if she bought the dress with a 30% discount. rather than a 25% discount?

	ANSWER

[END OF PAPER]

11+ CSSE TEST
English

SET A

Practice Paper 2 - English

1 hour (plus 10 minutes reading)

First Name	
Middle Name	
Last Name	
School	
Date of Birth	

READ THE INSTRUCTIONS CAREFULLY

- Do not open your booklet until you are told to do so.

- Work as quickly as you can through ALL the questions.

- You have 10 minutes to read through the extract in the comprehension section.

- You then have 1 hour to complete all the questions.

COMPREHENSION

The following passage is from Alice's Adventures in Wonderland by Lewis Carroll.

There seemed to be no use in waiting by the little door, so she went back to the table, half hoping she might find another key on it, or at any rate a book of rules for shutting people up like telescopes: this time she found a little bottle on it, ('which certainly was not here before,' said
5 Alice,) and round the neck of the bottle was a paper label with the words 'DRINK ME' beautifully printed on it in large letters.

It was all very well to say 'Drink me,' but the wise, little Alice was not going to do that in a hurry. 'No I'll look first,' she said, 'and see whether it's marked "poison" or not:' for she had read several nice little histories
10 about children who had got burnt, and eaten up by wild beasts and other unpleasant things, all because they would not remember the simple rules their friends had taught them: such as, that a red-hot poker will burn you if you hold it too long; and that if you cut your finger very deeply with a knife, it usually bleeds; and she had never forgotten that, if you drink
15 much from a bottle marked 'poison,' it is almost certain to disagree with you, sooner or later.

However, this bottle was not marked 'poison,' so Alice ventured to taste it and finding it very nice, (it had, in fact, a sort of mixed flavour of cherry-tart, custard, pine-apple, roast turkey, toffee, and hot buttered
20 toast,) she very soon finished it off.

'What a curious feeling!' said Alice; 'I must be shutting up like a telescope.'

And so it was indeed: she was now only ten inches high, and her face brightened up at the thought that she was now the right size for
25 going through the little door into that lovely garden. First, however, she waited for a few minutes to see if she was going to shrink any further: she felt a little nervous about this, 'for it might end, you know,' said Alice to herself, 'in my going out altogether like a candle. I wonder what I shall be like then?' And she tried to fancy what the flame of a candle is like after
30 the candle is blown out, for she could not remember ever having seen such a thing.

After a while, finding that nothing more had happened, she decided
on going into the garden at once; but alas for poor Alice! When she got
to the door, she found she had forgotten the little golden key and when
35 she went back to the table for it, she found she could not possibly reach
it: she could see it quite plainly through the glass, and she tried her best
to climb up one of the legs of the table, but it was too slippery; and when
she had tired herself out with trying, the poor little thing sat down and
cried.

40 'Come, there's no use in crying like that!' said Alice to herself, rather
sharply; 'I advise you to leave off this minute!' She generally gave herself
very good advice, (though she very seldom followed it), and sometimes
she scolded herself so severely as to bring tears into her eyes; and once
she remembered trying to box her own ears for having cheated herself
45 in a game of croquet she was playing against herself, for this curious
child was very fond of pretending to be two people. 'But it's no use now,'
thought poor Alice, 'to pretend to be two people! Why, there's hardly
enough of me left to make one respectable person!'

Soon her eye fell on a little glass box that was lying under the table:
50 she opened it, and found in it a very small cake, on which the words 'EAT
ME' were beautifully marked in currants. 'Well, I'll eat it,' said Alice, 'and
if it makes me grow larger, I can reach the key; and if it makes me grow
smaller, I can creep under the door; so either way I'll get into the garden,
and I don't care which happens!'

55 She ate a little bit, and said anxiously to herself, 'Which way?
Which way?', holding her hand on the top of her head to feel which way
it was growing, and she was quite surprised to find that she remained the
same size: to be sure, this generally happens when one eats cake, but
Alice had got so much into the way of expecting nothing but out-of-the-
60 way things to happen, that it seemed quite dull and stupid for life to go
on in the common way.

So she set to work, and very soon finished off the cake.

QUESTION 1

> "However, this bottle was not marked 'poison,' so Alice ventured to taste it and finding it very nice..."

What does this say about Alice's character?

A - She does what she is told.

B - Alice throws caution to the wind.

C - Alice is a mischievious child.

1 mark

QUESTION 2

a) In lines 1 - 6, the author uses a simile. Write out the simile.

_____

_____

1 mark

b) What do you think the author is trying to suggest with this simile.

_____

_____

_____

2 marks

QUESTION 3

Which of the following best describes how Alice is represented in this extract? (Tick three boxes.)

A - Surprised

B - Naïve

C - Curious

D - Unhappy

E - Wise

F - Supportive

3 marks

QUESTION 4

In the extract, which four words suggest Alice as being shocked or intrigued? (Tick four boxes.)

A - Surprised

B - Brightened

C - Ventured

D - Forgotten

E - Curious

F - Cheated

G - Wonder

H - Disagree

4 marks

QUESTION 5

In this extract, Alice spends a lot of time speaking to herself. What does this say about the character of Alice?

_____

_____

_____

1 mark

QUESTION 6

Lewis Carroll makes reference to the change in Alice's size. Why do you think Carroll has done this?

_____

_____

_____

1 mark

QUESTION 7

Pick out three features from the extract which suggest innocence.

_____

_____

_____

3 marks

Select from the passage one word which most closely corresponds to the word or phrase listed below. We have provided you with a guideline as to where the word can be found.

A - Exquisitely	Lines 4 - 8
B - Displeasing	Lines 9 - 13
C - Generally	Lines 12 - 14
D - Gambled	Lines 15 - 20
E - Light up	Lines 20 - 25
F - Apprehensive	Lines 25 - 30
G - Obviously	Lines 35 - 40
H - Rarely	Lines 40 - 44
I - Sabotaged	Lines 40 - 44
J - Admirable	Lines 45 - 48
K - Bewildered	Lines 55 - 59
L - Typical	Lines 60 - 62

12 marks

QUESTION 9

Why do you think Alice is in search for adventure?

A - Alice wants to find new things and new places.

B - Alice wants to get closer to nature.

C - Alice is unhappy at home.

QUESTION 10

In the extract, the author refers to the term "poison". Which of the following words is most associated with this term?

A - Danger

B - Surprise

C - Natural

D - Life

QUESTION 11

In one sentence, explain what the author, Lewis Carroll, is trying to make the reader feel after reading this extract.

_____

_____

QUESTION 12

Why does the author use the phrase "red-hot poker"?

_____

_____

1 mark

QUESTION 13

Which three activities is Alice trying to do, or has accomplished? (Tick three boxes.)

A - Eat cake to make herself grow. ☐

B - Find another person for companionship. ☐

C - Drink the potion, to shrink in size. ☐

D - Obtain the golden key. ☐

E - Find an exit to return home. ☐

3 marks

QUESTION 14

Using the literary terms mentioned, write out an example for each from the text.

a) SIMILE

_____

1 mark

b) ALLITERATION

_____

1 mark

c) RHETORICAL QUESTION

_____

1 mark

d) IMAGERY

_____

1 mark

e) REPETITION

_____

1 mark

f) PERSONAL PRONOUN

_____

1 mark

QUESTION 15

How is Alice represented in this extract? Use descriptive sentences and include literary techniques and examples in your response.

_____

_____

_____

_____

_____

_____

_____

_____

_____

5 marks

APPLIED REASONING

You should spend 10 minutes on this section.

Complete the words using the same letter to end the first word and start the second word.

For example:

Boa(?) ribe

* Boat

* Tribe

QUESTION 1

frien (?) rive

1 mark

QUESTION 2

tast (?) dible

1 mark

> **Complete the words using the same letter for each gap.**
>
> *For example:*
>
> Po(?)er   (?)ater
>
> • Power
>
> • Water

QUESTION 3

(?)u(?)bled   fa(?)ily

1 mark

QUESTION 4

te(?)se   (?)a(?)(?)y

1 mark

QUESTION 5

Find five words that can be made using the word below. Each word must contain four letters.

REMOVE

1.

_____

2.

_____

3.

_____

4.

_____

5.

_____

5 marks

QUESTION 6

Find five words that can be made using the word below. Each word must contain four letters.

LEARN

1.

_____

2.

_____

3.

_____

4.

_____

5.

_____

CONTINUOUS WRITING

You should spend 20 minutes on these 2 questions (10 minutes on each).

QUESTION 1

In five or six sentences, describe who you most aspire to be. For example, role models could be a family member or celebrity. Make your writing as descriptive as possible.

_____

_____

_____

_____

_____

_____

_____

_____

_____

_____

_____

_____

_____

_____

QUESTION 2

In five or six sentences, write down clear instructions for crossing a road safely.

_____

_____

_____

_____

_____

_____

_____

_____

_____

_____

_____

_____

[END OF PAPER]

END OF SET A

SET A
Answer Booklet

Answers to Maths and English Papers.

Using the answers in this booklet, carefully add up the total marks for the papers in Set A.

The total marks for Set A is 120.

Use the table below to keep track of your score for each paper in Set A.

	MATHS	ENGLISH	TOTAL
SET A			

Maths Paper

Q1. **a) 3,132** • 987 + 2,145 = 3,132	*1 mark*
b) 21.94 • 15.09 + 6.85 = 21.94 $\begin{array}{r} 15.09 \\ + \ 6.85 \\ \hline 21.94 \\ \scriptstyle 1 \quad 1 \end{array}$	*1 mark*
Q2. **a) 7,328** • 7,985 − 657 = 7,328 • 'Difference' means 'subtract'.	*1 mark*
b) 6,900 • 46 × 150 = 6,900	*1 mark*

x	100	50
40	4,000	2,000
6	600	300

Total = 6,900

Q3. **a) 65.52** • 13 × 5.04 = 65.52	*1 mark*

x	500	4
10	5,000	40
3	1,500	12

Total = 6,552

- Two numbers came after the decimal point, so two numbers have to come after the decimal point in the answer = 65.52

b) 17

- $306 \div 18 = 17$

$$18 \overline{)306} \quad 017$$

Q4.

a) 23

- $552 \div 24 = 23$

$$24 \overline{)552} \quad 023$$

b) 70

- $21 \div 3 = 7$

- There was one number after decimal point, so this needs to be added = 70.

Q5.

a) ? = 7

- $64 + 843 = 907$

b) ? = 5

- $0.16 + 1.58 = 1.74$

c) ? = 9	*1 mark*
• 8,9**74** − 321 = 8,653	
d) ? = 4	*1 mark*
• **4** − 12 = −8	
e) ? = 5	*1 mark*
• 17 × 26**5** = 4,505	
f) ? = 2	*1 mark*
• 5.5 ÷ **2** = **2**.75	
Q6.	
a) 6 minutes	*1 mark*
• Reading along the bottom of the graph, you can see that the remote-control aeroplane was used for 6 minutes (0 - 6 minutes).	
b) 45 metres	*1 mark*
• Reading along the bottom of the graph, reading up from 5 minutes, you can see that the remote-control aeroplane was 45 metres above the ground.	
c) 1 minute	*1 mark*
• Reading along the side of the graph, you can see that, it took 1 minute to ascend 10 metres.	

Q7.	
a) 1	*1 mark*
• If you folded the cube together, opposite the 3 dots would be 1 dot.	
b) 1	*1 mark*
• If you folded the cube together, opposite the 3 dots would be 1 dot.	
c) 6	*1 mark*
• If you folded the cube together, opposite the 3 dots would be 6 dots.	
Q8.	
a) 7,200	*1 mark*
• P = 16	
• R = 18	
• A = 1	
• Y = 25	
• 16 × 18 × 1 × 25 = 7,200	
b) Your answer should look like this:	*1 mark*
LAMB MATE LIAR MEET	
• LAMB = 12 × 1 × 13 × 2 = 312	
• MATE = 13 × 1 × 20 × 5 = 1,300	
• LIAR = 12 × 9 × 1 × 18 = 1,944	
• MEET = 13 × 5 × 5 × 20 = 6,500	

• The question requires you to list the words, beginning with lowest.	
c) F	*1 mark*
• NEW = 14 + 5 + 23 = 42	
• BAD = 2 + 1 + 4 = 7	
• 42 ÷ 7 = 6	
• The sixth letter in the alphabet is 'F'.	
Q9.	
a) 1 banana	*1 mark*
• If 3 bananas are used for 6 people, you need to divide this by the number of people, and then multiply it by how many people you are trying to work out.	
• 3 ÷ 6 = 0.5	
• 0.5 × 2 = 1	
b) 30 mangoes and 60 oranges	*1 mark*
• Mangoes = 3 ÷ 6 = 0.5	
• 0.5 x 60 = 30 mangoes	
• Oranges = 6 ÷ 6 = 1	
• 1 × 60 = 60 oranges	
Q10.	
a) False	*1 mark*
• The lowest temperature was 6°.	

b) True	*1 mark*
• The highest temperature was 16°C. The lowest temperature was 6°C. Therefore the difference was 16 − 6 = 10°C.	
c) True	*1 mark*
• The temperature in April was 10°C. The temperature in June was 16°C. Therefore the temperature did rise 6°C.	
d) False	*1 mark*
• The largest temperature fall occurred between July-Aug and Aug-Sept.	
Q11. C	*1 mark*
• Three quarters of 16 is 12. Therefore 12 squares need to be shaded in.	
Q12.	
a) 99,743	*1 mark*
b) 34,799	*1 mark*
c) 37,994	*1 mark*
Q13.	
a) 9	*1 mark*

b) 7

Q14.

a) 72

- Mon = 16
- Tues = 14
- Wed = 21
- Thurs = 9
- Fri = 12
- 16 + 14 + 21 + 9 + 12 = 72

b) 14.4

- If 72 ladybirds were seen throughout the week, we need to work out the average number of ladybirds seen per day.
- 72 ÷ 5 = 14.4

Q15.

a) 2 out of 40 OR 1 out of 20

b) Poppy is correct

Prime numbers between 1 and 40 = 2, 3, 5, 7, 11, 13, 17, 19, 23, 29, 31 and 37. There are 12 prime numbers between 1 and 40.

Factors of 12 = 1, 2, 3, 4, 6, 12. There are 6 factors of 12.

Therefore Poppy is correct that she is twice as likely to get a prime number than a factor of 12.

1 mark

1 mark

1 mark

1 mark

1 mark

c) Poppy is NOT correct

Prime numbers between 1 and 40 = 2, 3, 5, 7, 11, 13, 17, 19, 23, 29, 31 and 37. There are 12 prime numbers between 1 and 40.

Multiples of 3 = 3, 6, 9, 12, 15, 18, 21, 24, 27, 30, 33, 36, 39. There are 13 multiples of 3 between 1 and 40.

Therefore Poppy is NOT correct that she is more likely to have a prime number than a multiple of 3.

1 mark

Q16. Your answer should look like this:

1 mark

1.4	1.8	2.2
0.8	1.25	1.7
0.2	0.7	1.2

Q17.

a) 54.75

1 mark

- 56 + 50 + 52 + 61 + 67 + 60 + 60 + 32 = 438

- 438 ÷ 8 = 54.75

b) 35

1 mark

- 67 − 32 = 35

Q18.

a) 50 - 34 = 16   *1 mark*

- This question is trial and error.

b) 411 + 389 = 800   *1 mark*

- This question is trial and error.

c) 34 + (12 × 3) = 70   *1 mark*

- This question is trial and error.

d) 3,976 + (10 × 40) = 4,476   *1 mark*

- This question is trial and error.

Q19.

Your answer should look like this: *1 mark*

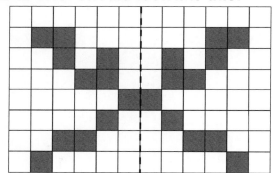

Q20.

a) False   *1 mark*

- Not all quadrilaterals are parallelograms.

b) True   *1 mark*

- All parallelograms are quadrilaterals.

c) True   *1 mark*

- A parallelogram with 4 perpendicular diagonals is called a rhombus.

Q21.Your answer should look like this:

| 2 | x | 1 | 4 | = | 2 | 8 |

1 mark

Q22.

a) 2

- 2 is the only prime number that is even.

1 mark

b) 4, 16 and 36

- $2 \times 2 = 4$
- $4 \times 4 = 16$
- $6 \times 6 = 36$

1 mark

c) 3, 5, and 11

- $3 \times 5 \times 11 = 165$

1 mark

Q23.

a) 2

b) 12

c) 33

+1	-3	+2	-3
5	6	3	3
+3	-3	+4	-3
2	5	2	6
+5	-3	+6	-3
3	8	5	11
+7	-3	+8	-3
8	15	12	20
+9	-3	+10	-3
17	26	23	33

1 mark

1 mark

1 mark

Q24.

a) £48.75

- $65 \div 100 = 0.65$
- $0.65 \times 25 = 16.25$
- £65.00 − £16.25 = £48.75

b) £3.25

- $65 \div 100 = 0.65$
- $0.65 \times 30 = 19.50$
- £65.00 − £19.50 = £45.50
- Using your answer to (part a) = £48.75 − £45.50 = £3.25

English Paper

Q1. B - Alice throws caution to the wind.	*1 mark*
• The phrase 'throws caution to the wind' is indicative of reckless behaviour. Although Alice does not drink the potion until she's checked the label, she is still very quick to taste the unknown substance, and her check to see if it was poison (or could harm her) was far from rigorous. By doing this, the author conveys how Alice's curiosity far outweighs her caution, and indeed her wisdom.	
Q2.	
a) shutting people up like telescopes	*1 mark*
• This sentence uses the word "like" which demonstrates that it is a simile.	
b) Your answer should be along the lines of:	*2 marks*
• The phrase, "shutting people up like telescopes" is most likely referring to making someone smaller. "Shutting up" doesn't necessarily mean to make someone quiet, but to "shut up" i.e. to make smaller, like a telescope when it's put away after being used.	

Q3. The three boxes that you should have ticked are: • B - Naïve • C - Curious • E - Surprised	*3 marks*
Q4. The four boxes that you should have ticked are: • Surprised (line 57) • Ventured (line 17) • Curious (line 21) • Wonder (line 28)	*4 marks*
Q5. Your answer should be along the lines of: • Alice speaks to herself as a sign of showing how lonely her character is. The fact that she is seeking adventures suggests that Alice is not satisfied with her life and wishes to change it. The fact that she talks to herself reminds the reader that Alice only wants companionship, and is young and naïve.	*1 mark*
Q6. You answer should resemble the following: • The author conveys Alice's character in different sizes – small and normal-sized. This is emphasised when she drinks the potion and shrinks to "ten inches tall". The author does this to illustrate fantasy; "I must be shutting up like a telescope".	*1 mark*

Q7. Below we have outlined a few examples that you could have written. Three are required:	*3 marks*
• She drinks the poison regardless.	
• She talks to herself. This shows innocence as children tend to talk to themselves when they are playing or thinking.	
• She's adventurous, yet doesn't know what she's getting herself into.	
Q8.	*12 marks*
• **A** - Exquisitely = "Beautifully"	
• **B** - Displeasing = "Unpleasant"	
• **C** - Generally = "Usually"	
• **D** - Gambled = "Ventured"	
• **E** - Light up = "Brightened"	
• **F** - Apprehensive = "Nervous"	
• **G** - Obviously = "Plainly"	
• **H** - Rarely = "Seldom"	
• **I** - Sabotaged = "Cheated"	
• **J** - Admirable = "Respectable"	
• **K** - Bewildered = "Surprised"	
• **L** - Typical = "Common"	

Q9. A - Alice wants to find new things and new places. • Alice is searching for adventures in this extract which suggests that she is looking for new, exciting things in her life. •	*1 mark*
Q10. The one box that you should have ticked was: • A - Danger	*1 mark*
Q11. Your answer should read along the lines of: • From reading the extract, the author is trying to demonstrate that Alice is a character full of curiosity and loneliness.	*1 mark*
Q12. Your answer should read along the lines of: • The author uses the phrase "red-hot poker" to signify danger and the importance of understanding your actions before you do something.	*1 mark*
Q13. The three boxes that you should have ticked are: • A - Eat cake to make herself grow. • C - Drink the potion, to shrink in size. • D - Obtain the golden key.	*3 marks*
Q14. **a) Simile = "in my going out altogether like a candle" (line 28)**	*1 mark*

b). Alliteration = "large letters" (line 6)	*1 mark*
c) Rhetorical Question = "I wonder what I shall be like then?" (line 28 and 29)	*1 mark*
d) Imagery = it had, in fact, a sort of mixed flavour of cherry-tart, custard, pine-apple..." (line 18 and 19)	*1 mark*
e) Repetition = 'Which way? Which way?' (line 55 and 56)	*1 mark*
f) Personal Pronoun = 'I advise you to leave off this minute!' (line 41)	*1 mark*
Q15. You could have written anything about Alice's character. For example, here are a few things you could have written about: • Alice is portrayed as smart. • Alice is portrayed as naïve and childish. • Alice is portrayed as a loner. *Remember to support your writing using literary techniques and quotes from the extract.	*5 marks*

APPLIED REASONING	
Q1. • friend • drive	*1 mark*
Q2. • taste • edible	*1 mark*
Q3. • mumbled • family	*1 mark*
Q4. • tense • nanny	*1 mark*
Q5. You could have written any five of the following: • Ever • Mere • More • Move • Over • Veer	*5 marks*

Q5. You could have written any five of the following:	5 marks
• Earl • Earn • Lane • Lean • Near • Real	

CONTINUOUS WRITING

Q1. You could have written something along the lines of:

- The person I look up to most, and most aspire to be is my mum. My mum is one of the most beautiful, strong-minded, and determined people that I know. Without her, I simply would not be who I am today...

Things to consider:

- You should try to make the examiner feel as though they could really imagine themselves being with the person you are describing.

- Try including imagery, or sensory descriptions: why is that person your role model? What do they do and why do you aspire to be like them? By explaining these things, you are painting a picture in the examiner's mind of the type of person you are.

- Try and include a few literary techniques. When you are using these, see if you can be creative. The examiner is looking for something original and different. Similes, metaphors and alliteration are all great techniques to make use of in these kinds of questions.

Q2. You could have written something along the lines of:

- To cross a road safely, first of all, you need to find a safe place to cross. The safest place to cross is via a pedestrian crossing. If you cannot find a pedestrian crossing, make sure you cross somewhere that you can see traffic clearly. Next, you will stand near the kerb (not too close as to be knocked off your feet), and look both left and right a few times...

Things to consider:

- For this question, it makes sense to think more about the structure before you begin your answer. If you plan this at the beginning, even if it's just quickly in your head, it will ensure that your piece of writing flows well. This is very important when composing your piece, as you don't want it to appear disjointed and confusing.

- Think about how you would cross a road. What would you do? How have your parents/guardians taught you to cross the road?

- Go into detail with your answer. The examiner does not want to read hundreds of papers all giving the same type of description. If you can, try and think of at least one small thing to make your piece original.

11+ CSSE TEST
Maths

SET B

Practice Paper 1 - Maths

60 minutes

First Name	
Middle Name	
Last Name	
School	
Date of Birth	

READ THE INSTRUCTIONS CAREFULLY

- Do not open your booklet until you are told to do so.
- Work as quickly as you can through ALL the questions.
- You have 60 minutes to answer ALL the questions.
- Calculators are NOT permitted during the test.

QUESTION 1

a) Calculate: 4,235 + 869

	ANSWER
4,235 869 5,104 × × ×	5,104

b) Add 40.59 and 103.87

	ANSWER
103.87 40.59 144.46 × ×	144.46

QUESTION 2

a) Work out the difference between: 12,698 and 3,589

	ANSWER
12,698 3,589 9,109	9,109

b) Calculate: 32 × 55

	ANSWER
32 55 160 1× 160 1600 1760	1760

QUESTION 3

a) What is the result of 15 multiplied by 2.4?

$\begin{array}{r} 15 \\ 2\cdot4 \\ \hline 36\cdot0 \end{array}$

	ANSWER
$1.5 \times 4 \quad \begin{array}{r}15\\2.4\\\hline0\cdot60\\30\cdot0\end{array} \quad \begin{array}{r}0.60\\30\end{array}$	36.0

1 mark

b) Calculate: 1,869 ÷ 21

	ANSWER
$2\sqrt{1869}$ $21\overline{)1869}$ $\begin{array}{r}21\ 1\\42\ 2\\63\ 3\\84\ 4\\105\ 5\\126\ 6\\147\ 7\\168\ 8\\189\end{array}$	$\begin{array}{r}889\\186\\168\\\hline018\end{array}$

1 mark

QUESTION 4

a) Divide 667 by 29

	ANSWER
$29\overline{)667}$ $\begin{array}{r}29\\58\\87\end{array}$ $23 \times 29 =$	23

1 mark

b) Calculate: 50 ÷ 0.8

$6\sqrt{40^4}$ $8\sqrt{50}$ $40 \div 0.6$

	ANSWER
$50\sqrt{6.125}$ $\begin{array}{r}50\\0.125\\\hline OSO\\2\end{array}$	$\begin{array}{r}62.5\\66.75\end{array}$

$8\sqrt{50}$ $6\sqrt{4.8}$

1 mark

Each of the following calculations is incomplete. Each calculation contains a question mark (?). For each question, work out the value of the question mark.

QUESTION 5

a) 84 + 394 = 4?8

	ANSWER
84 394 478	7

b) 0.58 + 7.?4 = 8.52

	ANSWER
0.58 − 8.52 8.52 0.58 7.94	9

c) 1?,345 − 594 = 11,751

	ANSWER
594 11,751 12,345	2

d) 103 − 584 = −4?1

	ANSWER

1 mark

e) 23 × 9? = 2,070

	ANSWER

1 mark

f) 7.7 ÷ 4 = 1.92?

	ANSWER

1 mark

QUESTION 6

40 children were asked how many siblings they have. The results were recorded using a bar chart.

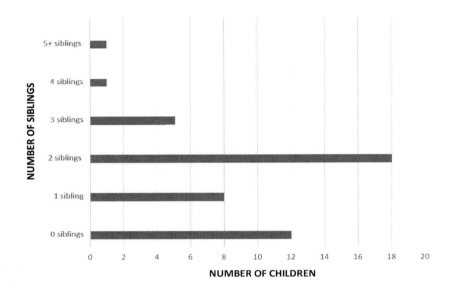

a) How many children have 3 siblings?

	ANSWER

1 mark

b) How many siblings did the children have altogether?

	ANSWER

1 mark

c) How many children had more than 2 siblings?

	ANSWER

1 mark

QUESTION 7

Using the below nets, work out how many dots would appear on the face OPPOSITE the side with 6 dots.

a)

1 mark

b)

1 mark

c)

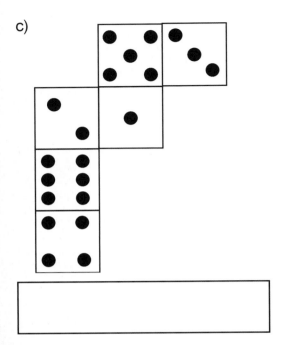

<table>
<tr><td></td></tr>
</table>

1 mark

QUESTION 8

For the following questions, there is one digit wrong in each calculation. They can be corrected by changing one digit in each question to the number **9**.

For the following questions, find out which digit should be replaced and re-write the calculation underneath so that it is correct.

a)   481 + 845 = 1,336

	ANSWER

1 mark

b)   6,362 − 2,457 = 3,605

	ANSWER

1 mark

c)   645 + (5 × 15) = 1,020

	ANSWER

1 mark

QUESTION 9

Below is a sketch of a field.

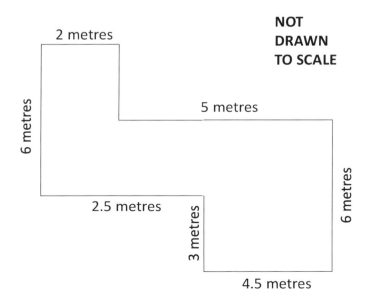

NOT DRAWN TO SCALE

a) What is the total area of the field?

	ANSWER

1 mark

b) What is the perimeter of the field?

	ANSWER

1 mark

QUESTION 10

Assume that the letters of the alphabet have the following ascending values:

A = 1, B = 2, C = 3, D = 4 and so on. Answer the following questions by adding up the values of the letters.

For example, the word DARK = 4 + 1 + 18 + 11 = a value of 34

a) What is the value of the word BEHAVE?

	ANSWER

1 mark

b) Using the same letter value system, sort the following words in ascending order according to value (lowest to highest).

BATHE | STARS | DRESS | PRIDE

1._____ 2._____ 3._____ 4._____

c) Which single letter has the same value as the result of dividing the sum total for 'PLAY' by the sum total of 'CAN'?

PLAY ÷ CAN =

	ANSWER

QUESTION 11

a) How many grams are there in 6.5kg?

	ANSWER

b) A jug contains 5.82 litres. How much is this in ml?

	ANSWER

1 mark

QUESTION 12

Below is a table of values for the formula 3(n + 8). Complete the table.

n	3 (n + 8)
6	42
9	
	69

3 marks

QUESTION 13

In each part of this question, the number can be made by multiplying two prime numbers together.

Write the two prime numbers in the empty boxes.

a)

	x		=	299

1 mark

b)

	X		=	77

QUESTION 14

a) A bottle contains 5.65 litres. How many millilitres is that?

	ANSWER

b) A bag of sugar contains 3,045g. Rewrite this quantity in kilograms.

	ANSWER

c) Add together: 5mm, 0.4cm, and 0.2m. Give your answer in cm.

	ANSWER

d) The area of a piece of card is calculated as:

9cm × 5.5cm = 49.5cm².

What is the area of the card in mm?

	ANSWER

QUESTION 15

Fill in the missing numbers in these fraction calculations.

a)

$$\frac{5}{10} + \frac{\boxed{2}}{10} = \frac{7}{10}$$

b)

$$\frac{1}{6} + \frac{3}{4} = \frac{11}{\boxed{12}}$$

c)

$$\frac{\overset{12}{\cancel{4}}}{7} + \frac{\overset{7}{\cancel{1}}}{3} = \frac{\boxed{19}}{21}$$

1 mark

QUESTION 16

Fill in the missing symbol. For example, >, < or =.

a) £5.20 $\boxed{=}$ 520p

1 mark

b) 4km $\boxed{>}$ 4000m

1 mark

c) 100cm $\boxed{<}$ 10m

1 mark

QUESTION 17

Look carefully at the patterned sequence.

  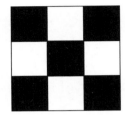 

a) How many black squares are needed for the 9th pattern?

	ANSWER

1 mark

b) How many squares would be needed in total for the 12th pattern?

	ANSWER

1 mark

c) If each square was calculated to be 15mm by 15mm, what would the total area of white squares be in pattern 8?

	ANSWER

QUESTION 18

I think of a number.

I subtract 12, and then multiply it by 7.

I halve the number and multiply by 3.

My number is now 84.

What number did I originally start with?

	ANSWER

QUESTION 19

The following machine shows a Maths calculation.

INPUT ——— × 7 ——— − 6 ——— OUTPUT

a) If the output of the machine was 71, what was the input of the machine?

77	ANSWER
	11

b) If the input of the machine was 0.6, what would the output of the machine be?

4·2	ANSWER
	−2·2

c) If the output of the machine was −20, what was the input of the machine?

	ANSWER

1 mark

QUESTION 20

For the following statements, tick whether they are true or false.

a) A quadrilateral will ALWAYS have one angle less than or equal to 90°.

TRUE	FALSE

1 mark

b) A square is the only quadrilateral to have four 90° angles.

TRUE	FALSE

1 mark

c) A trapezium has no rotational symmetry.

TRUE	FALSE

1 mark

QUESTION 21

Below is a spinner with the numbers **6**, **9**, **10**, **21**, **24** and **54**.

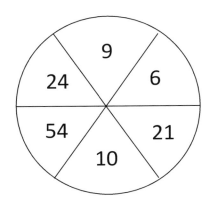

a) What is the probability of the spinner landing on an **odd number**?
Write your answer as a fraction in its simplest form.

	ANSWER

1 mark

b) What is the probability of the spinner landing on a **square number**?
Write your answer as a fraction.

	ANSWER

1 mark

QUESTION 22

A sequence uses the following rule:

$$n^{th} \text{ term} = 3(n + 1)$$

a) Work out the first 6 terms using the rule above.

1st term	2nd term	3rd term	4th term	5th term	6th term

1 mark

b) Explain how you know that the number **46** is not in the above sequence.

_____

_____

_____

_____

2 marks

[END OF PAPER]

11+ CSSE TEST
English

TOTAL SCORE

out of 60

SET B

Practice Paper 2 - English

1 hour (plus 10 minutes reading)

First Name	
Middle Name	
Last Name	
School	
Date of Birth	

READ THE INSTRUCTIONS CAREFULLY

- Do not open your booklet until you are told to do so.

- Work as quickly as you can through ALL the questions.

- You have 10 minutes to read through the extract in the comprehension section.

- You then have 1 hour to complete all the questions.

COMPREHENSION

The following passage is from The Secret Garden by Frances Hodgson Burnett.

"Look out of the window in about ten minutes and you'll see," the woman answered. "We've got to drive five miles across Missel Moor before we get to the Manor. You won't see much because it's a dark night, but you can see something."

5 Mary asked no more questions but waited in the darkness of her corner, keeping her eyes on the window. The carriage lamps cast rays of light a little distance ahead of them and she caught glimpses of the things they passed. After they had left the station they had driven through a tiny village and she had seen whitewashed cottages and the lights of a
10 public house. Then they had passed a church and a vicarage and a little shop-window or so in a cottage with toys and sweets and odd things set out for sale. Then they were on the highroad and she saw hedges and trees. After that there seemed nothing different for a long time—or at least it seemed a long time to her.

15 At last the horses began to go more slowly, as if they were climbing up-hill, and presently there seemed to be no more hedges and no more trees. She could see nothing, in fact, but a dense darkness on either side. She leaned forward and pressed her face against the window just as the carriage gave a big jolt.

20 "Eh! We're on the moor now sure enough," said Mrs. Medlock.

The carriage lamps shed a yellow light on a rough-looking road which seemed to be cut through bushes and low-growing things which ended in the great expanse of dark apparently spread out before and around them. A wind was rising and making a singular, wild, low, rushing
25 sound.

"It's—it's not the sea, is it?" said Mary, looking round at her companion.

"No, not it," answered Mrs. Medlock. "Nor it isn't fields nor mountains, it's just miles and miles and miles of wild land that nothing grows on but heather and gorse and broom, and nothing lives on but wild ponies and sheep."

"I feel as if it might be the sea, if there were water on it," said Mary. "It sounds like the sea just now."

"That's the wind blowing through the bushes," Mrs. Medlock said. "It's a wild, dreary enough place to my mind, though there's plenty that likes it—particularly when the heather's in bloom."

On and on they drove through the darkness, and though the rain stopped, the wind rushed by and whistled and made strange sounds. The road went up and down, and several times the carriage passed over a little bridge beneath which water rushed very fast with a great deal of noise. Mary felt as if the drive would never come to an end and that the wide, bleak moor was a wide expanse of black ocean through which she was passing on a strip of dry land.

"I don't like it," she said to herself. "I don't like it," and she pinched her thin lips more tightly together.

The horses were climbing up a hilly piece of road when she first caught sight of a light. Mrs. Medlock saw it as soon as she did and drew a long sigh of relief.

"Eh, I am glad to see that bit," she exclaimed. "It's the light in the lodge window. We shall get a good cup of tea after a bit, at all events."

It was "after a bit," as she said, for when the carriage passed through the park gates there was still two miles of avenue to drive through and the trees (which nearly met overhead) made it seem as if they were driving through a long dark vault.

They drove out of the vault into a clear space and stopped before an immensely long but low-built house which seemed to ramble round a stone court. At first Mary thought that there were no lights at all in the windows, but as she got out of the carriage she saw that one room in a corner upstairs showed a dull glow.

QUESTION 1

Out of the following options best describes the tone of the extract?

A - Optimistic.

B - Apprehensive.

C - Suspicious.

D - Exciting.

E - Pessimistic.

1 mark

QUESTION 2

"The carriage passed over a little bridge beneath which water rushed"

Which of the words in this sentence is a preposition?

A - Carriage

B - The

C - Little

D - Beneath

E - Rushed

2 marks

QUESTION 3

Which of the following best describes how the moor is represented? (Tick three boxes.)

A - Tame ☐

B - Wild ☐

C - Unnatural ☐

D - Drab ☐

E - Tranquil ☐

F - Desolate ☐

3 marks

QUESTION 4

In the extract, which four words suggest the mood the author is trying to create? (Tick four boxes.)

A - Unsettled ☐

B - Fascinating ☐

C - Idyllic ☐

D - Dubious ☐

E - Melancholic ☐

F - Isolated ☐

G - Upbeat ☐

H - Mysterious ☐

4 marks

QUESTION 5

"The wide, bleak moor was a wide expanse of black ocean"

What literary technique is this?

_____

2 marks

QUESTION 6

Why do you think Mary asks "it's not the sea, is it?"

_____

_____

_____

2 marks

QUESTION 7

Pick out three features from the extract which show Mary's concerns.

_____

_____

_____

3 marks

QUESTION 8

Select from the passage one word which most closely corresponds to the word or phrase listed below. We have provided you with a guideline as to where the word can be found.

A - Peep	Lines 5 - 10
B - Not the same	Lines 11 - 13
C - In a minute	Lines 13 - 16
D - Solid	Lines 15 - 20
E - Stretch	Lines 20 - 24
F - Supposedly	Lines 20 - 24
G - Remarkable	Lines 20 - 24
H - Hedge	Lines 31 - 36
I - Quickly	Lines 36 - 40
J - Shining	Lines 45 - 48
K - Safe	Lines 50 - 55
L - Extremely	Lines 55 - 59

12 marks

QUESTION 9

What type of words are these:

bushes   mountains   sheep

A - Abstract nouns

B - Proper nouns

C - Common nouns

D - Pronouns

QUESTION 10

Instead of using the word "said" in the extract, the author also uses other ways to say the same thing. List all of the alternatives.

_____

_____

_____

_____

_____

QUESTION 11

How does the extract make YOU (as the reader) feel? You should support your answer with quotes from the extract.

_____

_____

_____

_____

_____

_____

3 marks

QUESTION 12

What does Mrs Medlock's "sigh of relief" suggest?

A - That she was tired

B - That she was overwhelmed

C - That she was relieved

D - That she was hot

1 mark

QUESTION 13

The author speaks about "dense darkness". What is "dense darkness"? Answer using an adjective and a noun.

_____

_____

_____

2 marks

111

QUESTION 14

In the lines 20 - 25, the author uses the sentence "a wind was rising and making a singular, wild, low, rushing sound." By looking at the way the author uses tone of voice, see if you can explain, in your own words, what **singular** means.

It means...

_____

_____

_____

_____

3marks

APPLIED REASONING

You should spend 10 minutes on this section.

Each question below contains a word with 3 missing letters. The missing letters all have the same pattern. The second missing letter is three further on in the alphabet than the first. The third missing letter is one further on in the alphabet.

For example:

D(?)y(?)r(?)am

- This word would be daydream.

- The letter 'd' is four further from 'a'. The third letter is one further from the second.

QUESTION 1

p(?)d(?)(?)d

	Word =

QUESTION 2

s(?)(?)(?)

	Word =

Complete the words using the same letter for each gap.

For example:

Stati(?)n   (?)pal

- Station

- Opal

QUESTION 3

s(?)acious   (?)heasant

? =

2 marks

QUESTION 4

amic(?)ble   l(?)vish

? =

2 marks

QUESTION 5

esti(?)ate   pro(?)pt

? =

2 marks

QUESTION 6

Find five words that can be made using the word below. Each word must contain four letters.

IDEAL

1.

_____

2.

_____

3.

_____

4.

_____

5.

_____

5 marks

QUESTION 7

Find five words that can be made using the word below. Each word must contain four letters.

SOUTH

1.

2.

3.

4.

5.

5 marks

CONTINUOUS WRITING

You should spend 20 minutes on these 2 questions (10 minutes on each).

QUESTION 1

In five or six sentences, describe your ideal job. Be sure to include descriptive sentences to explain why you want that job, and what you would enjoy most from it.

_____

_____

_____

_____

_____

_____

_____

_____

_____

_____

_____

_____

_____

_____

QUESTION 2

In five or six sentences, write down clear instructions for baking a cake.

_____

_____

_____

_____

_____

_____

_____

_____

_____

_____

_____

_____

_____

_____

[END OF PAPER]

END OF SET B

11+ CSSE TEST
Set B

SET B
Answer Booklet

Answers to Maths and English Papers.

Using the answers in this booklet, carefully add up the total marks for the papers in Set B.

The total marks for Set B is 120.

Use the table below to keep track of your score for each paper in Set B.

	MATHS	ENGLISH	TOTAL
SET B			

Maths Paper

Q1.	
a) 5,104	*1 mark*
• 4,235 + 869 = 5,104	
b) 144.46	*1 mark*
• 40.59 + 103.87 = 144.46	
Q2.	
a) 9,109	*1 mark*
• 12,698 − 3,589 = 9,109	
b) 1,760	*1 mark*
• 32 × 55 = 1,760	
Q3.	
a) 36	*1 mark*
• 15 × 2.4 = 36	
b) 89	*1 mark*
• 1,869 ÷ 21 = 89	

Q4.	
a) 23	*1 mark*
• $667 \div 29 = 23$	
b) 62.5	*1 mark*
• $50 \div 0.8 = 62.5$	
Q5.	
a) ? = 7	*1 mark*
• $84 + 394 = 47\mathbf{7}8$	
b) ? = 9	*1 mark*
• $0.58 + 7.?4 = 8.52$	
• $8.52 - 0.58 = 7.\mathbf{9}4$	
c) ? = 2	*1 mark*
• $1?,345 - 594 = 11,751$	
• $11,751 + 594 = 1\mathbf{2},345$	
d) ? = 8	*1 mark*
• $103 - 584 = -48\mathbf{1}$	
e) ? = 0	*1 mark*
• $23 \times 9? = 2,070$	
• $2,070 \div 23 = 9\mathbf{0}$	

f) ? = 5 $7.7 \div 4 = 1.925$	*1 mark*
Q6. **a) 5** • Reading the bar graph, it shows that 5 children had 3 siblings.	*1 mark*
b) 68 • $5 + 4 + 15 + 36 + 8 = 68$	*1 mark*
c) 7 • $5 + 1 + 1 = 7$	*1 mark*
Q7. **a) 1** • If you folded the dice, the face with 6 dots will be directly opposite the face with 1 dot.	*1 mark*
b) 3 • If you folded the dice, the face with 6 dots will be directly opposite the face with 3 dots.	*1 mark*
c) 5 • If you folded the dice, the face with 6 dots will be directly opposite the face with 5 dots.	*1 mark*

Q8.	
a) 491 + 845 = 1,336	*1 mark*
b) 6,362 − 2,457 = 3,905	*1 mark*
c) 945 + (5 × 15) = 1,020	*1 mark*

Q9.

a) 40.5m^2   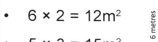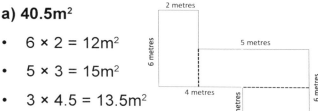   *1 mark*

- $6 \times 2 = 12m^2$
- $5 \times 3 = 15m^2$
- $3 \times 4.5 = 13.5m^2$
- $12 + 15 + 13.5 = 40.5m^2$

b) 32m   *1 mark*

- $2 + 3 + 5 + 6 + 4.5 + 3 + 2.5 + 6 = 32m$

Q10.

a) 43   *1 mark*

- $2 + 5 + 8 + 1 + 22 + 5 = 43$

b) Bathe   Pride   Dress   Stars   *1 mark*

- Bathe = 36
- Pride = 52
- Dress = 65
- Stars = 77

c) C

- Play = 54
- Can = 18
- 54 ÷ 18 = 3
- 3 = C

Q11.

a) 6,500g

- 1kg = 1,000g
- 6.5kg = 6,500g

b) 5,820

- 1l = 1,000ml
- 5.82 litres = 5,820 millilitres

Q12.

Your answer should look like this:

n	$3(n + 8)$
6	42
9	51
15	69

Q13.	
a) 13 and 23	*1 mark*
• 13 × 23= 299	
b) 7 and 11	*1 mark*
• 7 × 11 = 77	
Q14.	
a) 5,650 millilitres	*1 mark*
• 1l = 1,000ml	
• 5.65 litres = 5,650 millilitres	
b) 3.045kg	*1 mark*
• 1,000g = 1kg	
• 3,045g = 3.045kg	
c) 20.9cm	*1 mark*
• 5mm = 0.5cm	
• 0.4cm	
• 0.2m = 20 centimeters	
• 0.5 + 0.4 + 20 = 20.9cm	

d) 495mm²

- 49.5cm = 495mm

Q15.

a) 2

- 5 + 2 = 7
- $\frac{7}{10} + \frac{2}{10} = \frac{7}{10}$

b) 12

- 1 × 4 = 4
- 6 × 3 = 18
- 4 + 18 = 22 (numerator)
- 6 × 4 = 24 (denominator)
- Simplify $\frac{22}{24} = \frac{11}{12}$

c) $\frac{19}{21}$

- 4 × 3 = 12
- 7 × 1 = 7
- 12 + 7 = 19 (numerator)
- 7 × 3 = 21 (denominator)

1 mark

1 mark

1 mark

1 mark

Q16.	
a) =	*1 mark*
b) >	*1 mark*
c) <	*1 mark*
Q17.	
a) 41	*1 mark*
• Work out the first few patterns with the numbers provided. Apart from the 1st one, you will see that the pattern increases by 2. The pattern repeats once, before adding another 2.	
• The pattern is as follows:	
+1, +3, +3, +5, +5, +7, +7, +9, +9...	
b) 144	*1 mark*
• 12 × 12 = 144	
c) 7,200mm²	*1 mark*
• In the 8th pattern, there would be 32 white squares.	
• Each square is 15mm x 15mm = 225mm²	
• 225mm² × 32 = 7,200mm²	

Q18. 20 • $84 \div 3 = 28$ • $28 \times 2 = 56$ • $56 \div 7 = 8$ • $8 + 12 = 20$	*1 mark*
Q19. **a) 11** • $71 + 6 = 77$ • $77 \div 7 = 11$	*1 mark*
b) −1.8 • $0.6 \times 7 = 4.2$ • $4.2 - 6 = -1.8$	*1 mark*
c) −2 • $-20 + 6 = -14$ • $-14 \div 7 = -2$	*1 mark*
Q20. **a) TRUE** • At least one angle in a quadrilateral will be less than or equal to 90°.	*1 mark*
b) FALSE • Rectangles also have four 90° angles.	*1 mark*

c) TRUE	*1 mark*
• Trapeziums have no rotational symmetry.	
Q21.	
a) ⅓	*1 mark*
• There are 6 numbers on the spinner.	
• There are 2 numbers that are odd.	
• The probability of landing on an odd number would be ²⁄₆.	
• This would simplify to ⅓.	
b) ⅙	*1 mark*
• 9 is the only square number on the spinner.	
Q22.	
a) 6 9 12 15 18 21	*1 mark*
• N represents the term in the sequence. For example, the first term would be (1 + 1) × 3 = 6	
b) Your answer should be along the lines of:	*2 marks*
• All of the terms are multiples of three. 46 is not a multiple of three. Therefore, the answer cannot be 46.	

ANSWERS TO SET B

English Paper

Q1. E - Pessimistic • The whole extract is when in a pessimistic tone of voice.	*1 mark*
Q2. D - beneath • In this sentence, "beneath" is the preposition. This is because it is telling you whereabouts the water is in relation to the bridge.	*2 marks*
Q3. **B - Wild** **D - Drab** **F - Desolate** • These three words sum up the moor.	*3 marks*
Q4. **A - Unsettled** **D - Dubious** **E - Melancholic** **F - Isolated** • These four words sum up the author's mood.	*4 marks*

Q5. Metaphor	*2 marks*
• The moor is being compared to an ocean. However, it is not a simile because it does not use "as" or "like" in the description.	
Q6. Your answer should be along the lines of:	*2 marks*
• Mary asks "it's not the sea, is it?" to reiterate how there is nothing but darkness surrounding her.	
Q7. Below are a few answers that you could have had:	*3 marks*
• "Keeping her eyes on the window"	
• "There seemed nothing different for a long time"	
• "She could see nothing"	
• "I don't like it"	
• "She pinched her thin lips more tightly together"	
Q8. Your answer should look like this:	*12 marks*
• **A** - Peep - Glimpses	
• **B** - Not the same - Different	
• **C** - In a minute - Presently	
• **D** - Solid - Dense	
• **E** - Stretch - Expanse	
• **F** - Supposedly - Apparently	

- **G** - Remarkable - Great
- **H** - Hedge - Bushes
- **I** - Quickly - Rushed
- **J** - Shining - Light
- **K** - Safe - Vault
- **L** - Extremely - Immensely

Q9. C - Common nouns

2 marks

- Common nouns are nouns that don't require a capital letter. Common nouns are people, places or a thing that is not specific.

Q10. Below are all the words that you should have written down:

2 marks

- "answered"
- "exclaimed"

Q11. Your answer should be your personal opinion.

3 marks

- You could talk about how the extract makes you feel a sense of loneliness. You could refer to the darkness that is conveyed to emphasise uncertainty and isolation.

Q12. C - That she was relieved

1 mark

- Mrs Medlock's sigh of relief indicates that she was relieved to have arrived at the premises.

Q13. Your answer should be along the lines of:	2 marks
• The author uses alliteration in the phrase "dense darkness" to create a bigger impact. Darkness is the absence of light. Dense refers to something being closely compacted. This suggests that the darkness is compressive and heavy, making it feel even more dark and eerie.	
Q14. Your answer should be along the lines of:	3 marks
• It means that the sound of the wind sounded isolating and ominent. The singular sound suggests that nothing else could be heard, making it even more mysterious and nerve-wracking. This is crucial for creating the idea of seclusion and eeriness.	

APPLIED REASONING	
Q1. • padded	*1 mark*
Q2. • slop	*1 mark*
Q3. • spacious • pheasant	*2 marks*
Q4. • amicable • lavish	*2 marks*
Q5. • estimate • prompt	*2 marks*

Q6. You could have written any five of the following: • Aide • Deal • Deli • Dial • Idea • Idle • Laid • Lead • Lied	*5 marks*
Q7. You could have written any five of the following: • Host • Huts • Oust • Outs • Shot • Shut • Thou • Thus • Tosh	*5 marks*

CONTINUOUS WRITING

Q1. You could have written something along the lines of:

- I have always wanted to help people. That is why I think I would make a fantastic nurse. Being a nurse requires a lot of training, commitment, and integrity - all of which I think I possess...

Things to consider:

- You want to make the examiner feel as though they can understand your reasons for wanting a certain type of job.

- Try including imagery, or sensory descriptions: what does that job mean to you? By explaining these things, you are painting a picture in the examiner's mind of the type of person you are, and the person you want to become.

- Try and include a few literary techniques. When you are using these, see if you can be creative. The examiner is looking for something original and different. Similes, metaphors and alliteration are all great techniques to make use of in these kinds of questions.

Q2. You could have written something along the lines of:

- The first step to baking a cake is to make sure you have all of the correct ingredients. Before you begin prepping your ingredients, you should preheat the oven. Next, you can line your baking tray with cake cases...

Things to consider:

- For this question, it makes sense to think more about the structure before you begin your answer. If you plan this at the beginning, even if it's just quickly in your head, it will ensure that your piece of writing flows well. This is very important when composing your piece, as you don't want it to appear disjointed and confusing.

- Think about how you would bake a cake. What would you do? Have you ever helped someone bake a cake? What did they do?

- Go into detail with your answer. The examiner does not want to read hundreds of papers all giving the same type of description. If you can, try and think of at least one small thing to make your piece original.

IMPROVE YOUR ELEVEN PLUS ABILITY!

Get Access To
FREE
11+
TEST
QUESTIONS

www.MyEducationalTests.co.uk

Printed in Germany
by Amazon Distribution
GmbH, Leipzig